Dr Rithal —

I found this book at
a book fair and, of course,
thought of you. :)

Even though you probably have this one —
you can never have enough of it.

old Bud.

With affection,
Rolen Sweetman "BA" :)

I, BILLY SHAKESPEARE!

Also by William Peter Blatty

JOHN GOLDFARB, PLEASE COME HOME!
WHICH WAY TO MECCA, JACK?

I, BILLY SHAKESPEARE!

BY WILLIAM PETER BLATTY
Drawings by Victoria Chess

1965

DOUBLEDAY & COMPANY, INC., GARDEN CITY, NEW YORK

For Chris, Mike, and Mary Jo,
with love from
their father

EDITOR'S NOTE

The texts that follow are verbatim transcriptions taken from a series of six spoken-language tape recordings provided by an agency of the United States Government. Accompanying the tapes were the sketches interspersed with the text. Both tapes and sketches are alleged to be the product of the voice and hand of William Shakespeare of Stratford-on-Avon. We reserve our editorial judgment.

I, BILLY SHAKESPEARE!

TAPE ONE

You shagrag, shake-rotten, whoreson bulls' pizzles! Scurvy, lousy, vernaculous knaves! It is I—little Billy Shakespeare!

Surprised? Eh? You hey-passing, tomb-crawling, cryptographing squid! Who were you expecting? F. Bacon?

C. Marlowe? E. de Vere? A. the Hun? Well, false! Not applicable! None of the above! I am I—your fun-loving Bard of Avon! Yes! A *spook!* Wild, eh? There, there, God love you, I've frightened you, you suet, you Elynor Rummings, you shimmering first cousins to a cockle-cry-

ing toad. Rest. Me white magic, savvy? Prospero stuff!
Good juju! Ungawa!

Heh heh heh. You wonder how it is that I speak your
English so well? Eh? Manningtree oxen! What do you
suppose I've been *doing* in the hereafter? Writing *Iago
Meets Richard III?* Wise up, coz. People didn't stop dying
in 1616. We get lots of young moderns over here in the
Twilight Zone. And I've a sexy ear for dialogue. I listen.
Lately I've been listening to the likes of your "Papa" Hem-
ingway, and if he tells me one more time about that lion
in Kenya I'm going to send him *across* the river, *into* the
trees, and—! . . . Meanwhile, gulls, I have conned your
idiom under the tutelage of a certain Mr. James Dean,
formerly of Hollywood, California, and presently very
dead. But enough of small beer. To the matter, the matter,
the matter! The clearing up of the mystery!

So you'd like to know who wrote my plays, eh? Well,
I didn't write them, we *all* know *that*. I mean, my *name*
is on them, isn't it? If I had written them, why would
my *name* be on them? Why would my *contemporaries*
have testified that I wrote them? Why would all of England for *150 years afterward* have believed that I wrote
them? The answer is obvious to even the meanest in-
telligence: because I *didn't* write them!

Any questions? Eh? No hands? Splendid. But I am
prickled by tingly murmurings and beg to remind you of
what Ben Jonson said. He said that I had "little Latin and
less Greek." Yes. This is what we call a crusher, especially
when you consider that my plays were *written* in Latin
and Greek. You there, you with your hand up. What?
They were written in English? Nonsense! They were
translated into English. No, I grant you it isn't commonly

Myself addressing the Baconian Society

known, but even now German scientists are excavating two hundred feet beneath the Folger Library in Washington, D.C., and you may rest assured that their findings will confirm my statement. We have only to wait and the real William Shakespeare will stand up. In the meantime, do not be alarmed if Professor Frank Baxter tells you that when Ben made that snide remark, he was making it as part of a glowing tribute to *me* as the author of the plays. Whom can you trust on television these days? Moreover, any man who could write *The Alchemist* is obviously two-faced and not to be trusted. *Operatio sequitur esse* and all that. Know what I mean? Ben could be "had." Gotten to. Shmeared. And why not? Anyone realizing a net profit of only six pounds for a play like *Volpone* is welcome to all he can get. And Benny got. He was *paid* to write that simpering eulogy to me, *paid* to cover up. Paid by whom? Tush. That's classified information. Cosmic secret. Let's just say "authoritative sources." "*Certain* sources." "Sources close to the top." Eh?

Heh heh heh. I've been teasing. But now I'll tell. *Liz* wrote my plays! Not your Liz, dummy—*ours!* Liz One! The Queen!

Liz writing my plays (hah!)

Yes! Surprise surprise! I was Elizabeth's "ghost"!

Can you believe it? Of *course* you can. I *know* you can. All that sex drive had to be channeled *some*where, right? Certainly. Law of compensation, *ratio ingenii* and all that. After Essex, what etc. and—look, just trust me on this one, will you? Liz wrote the plays. Let's not even *argue* about it! And please, *please* don't ask me why she covered it up. I mean, how would it look for the Queen of England to be known as the author of lines like:

> . . . he had not been there, bless the
> mark, a pissing while but all the
> chamber smelt him. . . . When didst thou
> see me heave up my leg and make water
> against a gentlewoman's farthingale?

How would it have looked? *Eh?* Damn poor show for the Queen, *that's* how it would have looked! It would have been dis*a*ster!

Liz wrote them, all right. But look at you, you drab scullions, you slack-jawed skeptics. Want proof? Eh? Heh heh heh. Yes. Proof. Well, proof you shall have. As follows.

Liz was born September 7, 1533. Converted to all-number dialing, this yields the rather magical fantastical number:

$$97-15-33$$

So far, nothing. Right? Right! But wait a second. Wait! Assume that the "15" signifies the fifteenth "Shakespearean" (sic) play by date of composition. That would be *Henry IV, Part One*. The "33," then, would signify Act III, Scene 3. And if we add the "9" and the "7", totaling 16, we may proceed to the sixteenth speech by a charac-

ter in Act III, Scene 3 of *Henry IV, Part One*. Know
how that speech begins, dummy? It begins, "Now, as *I
am a true woman*"!!

Convinced? Eh? No. You want more. Lud, lud, where
is faith? But more you shall have. As follows. Multiplying
the 9 by the 7 yields 63. This, minus the last two digits
of our marvey magical number—33—yields 30. Now add
to that (you *can add*, can't you?) the *first* two digits of
our magical number—15—and our sum is 45. Forty-five.
Heh heh heh. Go ahead—count down forty-five lines
from the start of Act III, Scene 3. You will arrive, leek-
heads, at the words *"ignis fatuus."* Look at them. *Look!*
Do they tell you anything? Of course. They are Latin.
That *immediately* eliminates me as their author. But what
else? Do you see it? A little "God Save Our Gracious
Queen" in the background, friends. For when Liz was a
little girl she owned a sled that she adored. And the name
of that sled? *Ignis Fatuus!!!*

Now do you believe? Of *course*, you believe. I *know*
you believe. You'll believe *anything*, you swollen dropsies!
Good *God*, why should they mock poor fellows thus?!
Have I not had it? Eh? Who tweaks my beard and calls
me Bacon?! Why, that fop essayist! That penner of letters
to the *Times* who never wrote a hit play in his life! In
his *life*, boobies, in his *life!*

Or would you have me Marlowe?! Why, that flaming
atheist! Cloak-and-dagger faggot! In seven plays he writes
one quotable line—*one!*

> Is this the face that launched a
> thousand ships and burned the top-
> less towers of Ilium? . . .

Gil at work

Big deal, as Jimmy would say. It took a smart college kid to write *that* one, now, didn't it! My younger brother Gilbert wrote better lines on privy walls. And at least Gil signed them. Marlowe's "magnificent seven" appeared anonymously. Tell you anything, coz? Well, it tells *me* something. It tells me good riddance to bad rubbish when Marlowe got his in that tavern brawl at Deptford in '93. In the head, my darlings, he got it in the head: a knife

Marlowe being put out of his misery
(Can the world be all bad?)

wound over his right eye two inches deep and one wide!
Enough to kill an elk. Enough to kill a caribou. Enough
to kill a bison like Marlowe, in fact. But *no*, cries one of
your marvey researchers: "Marlowe lived on and he
wrote Billy's plays!" Of course. Why not? Marlowe, it is
known, had a wondrous power of clotting and your sur-
geons have even testified that a dagger thrust into the head
—especially if the head contain jelly—of some "six or
seven inches in depth and two inches in width need not

result in death at all. The patient might well have every prospect of living on, though mentally impaired." Splendid. Smashing. Crushing good point. You've got me there, coz, and I'll have to confess. Marlowe lived on. Yes—he lived! And continued to write anonymously. Unfortunately, he wrote only nonsense syllables and exclusively on the backs of envelopes and on stained-glass windows, a phenomenon largely attributable to the large and rather stunning metal plate in his head. He was arrested at last for throwing leeks at the Queen. His defense was "I'm crazy!" and the mob stoned him instanter. Satisfied now?

Marlowe in "drag"

Talk about bearing fardels! Whenever one of your scabrous scholars attributes one of my plays to Marlowe, he
shows up at meeting with that infuriating, fruity smirk,
lisps, "Hi, you pampered jades you," then turns directly
to me and cackles, "Oh, *hi*, Billsie; heard the latest?" That
bombastic, mocking, violet Cambridge dandy! That minc-
ing queen! Always before these sallies I spy him huddling
with a certain Mr. de Sade and I can only *guess* at the
nature of their relationship. Meanwhile, keep talking, you
Martlemas beeves who think he wrote my plays. Keep
talking. You're standing over a trapdoor. I'm *back!*

The Phantom Bard

Back where, *that* is the question. I don't know. No, really, I don't. I'm transparent, not omniscient. Phantoms have severely limited powers. In fact, they— . . . Heh heh heh. It just struck me. "The Phantom Bard." I like it.

I don't like this place—this room—this office. But I can't leave it. Oh, yes, my dears, back to *my* world, back along the yellow brick road to Big Disneyland. But I can't proceed farther into *your* world. Don't ask me why. I don't *know* why. Frankly, the whole enterprise reeks of the uncanny. It was one thing to write about the supernatural; that was just giving the crowd what it wanted; but participating in it is a phenomenon that I never had too clearly in mind as the terminal goal of my aspirations. I don't like it, Holmes, I don't like it. (You think Arthur Conan Doyle wrote those stories? You're crazy. It was Kaiser Wilhelm.)

We've all been clotting around on the "other side" just drifting and dreaming, waiting for the great ax to fall; waiting to be collected. At least that's the current "in" theory. I pray that a merciful God will make a special collection of Marlowe at His earliest possible convenience, for it would rid us all of a plentiful surfeit of hot air. The Papists have organized a "perpetual novena" for that express intention and I am rattling my beads with the rest of them.

This room. For all I know it is on a "Street in Venice." "A Heath." "The French Camp near Dover." "Birnam Wood." (Heh heh heh. See anything moving out there, coz?) It is sparsely fitted out: a wooden desk, two straight-backed wooden chairs, a painting, and mauve drapes that smell oddly of guava. No windows. But there is plentiful paper and pen and ink in the desk and I shall use them for illustrative sketches. As to my text, I had hoped for a typewriter for I am pure hell on handwriting. Check the records. Notice the wild spellings of my name? "Shagspere," "Shakysper," "Shaxberd," etc.? Now you know why. Handwriting. I didn't keep changing my name like Jonson. It used to be plain old "Benjamin Johnson," you know, but then he went London and swung out with "Ben Jonson." Today he'd be calling himself Rip Torn. Ah, well, every man in his humour. *Sic gloria est*, etc. By the way, that isn't Latin. It's Arabic. I don't *know* any Latin.

No typewriter. Too bad. I cannot dazzle you with the "cockroach" act. But there *is* a tape recorder. Convenient, eh? We call that a *deus ex machina*, stupid. In this case, a *machina ex machina*. Yes. Now you know it is I!

The recorder baffled me. True, there appeared to be operating instructions on the back, but unfortunately they are in Japanese and if there's a language I know "little" or "less" of, that's it, dear hearts, that's it. There is also some printing in Spanish appended, but I couldn't read that either. In my day Spanish was non-politic; non-popular; non-U. Tower of London and all that. My God, they *killed* you for it! One "*buenas noches*" and, WHIZ! Off went your thinkpiece!

It has taken me some few hours, but I believe I can manage the recorder passing well. We'll certainly find out when I play this back. But where to begin? The myths? Eh? The "horse-holding" bit? Heh heh heh. You marvelous fatheads! You really believe I started my London career holding horses for theatergoers? Or that I organized a runny-nosed union of little horse-holders called

Bard playing with tape recorder

"Shakespeare's Boys"? *Eh?* What do you take me for, a bloody *Scout*master?!

But soft. To the heart of the matter. Some sniveling coxcombs have put it abroad that I couldn't possibly have written my plays. The plays are too "great," too steeped in "erudition." And I'm stupid, see! I'm *dumb!* I'm the "son of an illiterate butcher"! And what about the manuscripts, Billy, the original texts? Where are they hidden and why? Secrets, see, spy stuff! Mumbo jumbo! Button button!

And then this business about *Hamlet*. Do you know what Freud has been telling me? Eh? Have you any *idea?* Talk about *filth!* Talk about—!

. . . I sense a presence in the neighbor room. The bearded gentleman whose portrait hangs above the desk? Tush. Light already. The morn, in russet mantle clad, walks o'er the dew of yon high eastern hill. Break we up our watch, etc. Remember that one? *Hamlet*, 1601. And then in 1602 I wrote— . . .

Anon!

TAPE TWO

Someone entered the room last night and it was clearly not A Messenger. It was the man in the portrait. He stood framed in the doorway just as I was fading. A sullen, sleepy-eyed brute, he wore blue and white striped pajamas and an Arden-green beret. I couldn't see much of his face beneath that rank and wild growth of black beard, but the nose put me very much in mind of Savonarola on his more manic days. Speaking of arsonists, could it be "The Beard" who is responsible for the noisome stink of cigar smoke in here? I think he saw me. Let us hope this does not lead to further interruptions.

But enough of small beer. 'Tis again the very witching time of night when churchyards moan, etc. etc. Where were we? Never mind, ass, it was a rhetorical question. I *know* where we were: in the wasteland of your snide conjectures.

So my father was a "greasy butcher," eh? And it offends

The Beard

you, does it, that one of the masses could have written
Lear, Macbeth, et al.? Yes, it offends you. I can *see* that
it offends you. So you had to ring in nobles and university
snots. Do me a favor, would you? Let me hear you say,
"Sweet lady, ho ho!" Excellent. You were born for the
part. And your opinions put me in mind of a certain Mr.
Marx over on the "other side" who has been peddling
some twaddlesome theories about the "capitalist mentality"
that at one time struck me as being false as dicers' oaths
but which I now find frabjiously appropriate. I wish I

could find him. But when he last approached me with a handful of tracts I fobbed him off on a certain Mr. Caligula and haven't seen him since. I trust they are getting along.

And how are *you* getting along? Enjoying this little seance, are you? Taking notes, eh, you vacant-eyed cretins, you overweening dolts? Well, set you down this: Will Shakespeare's father was not a butcher but a glover. His stall was set up in the paved market square of Stratford, and my *God*, he had to beat the customers off with the jawbone of a Marlowe. He traveled in *gloves!* Not hamhocks or chitlings! *Gloves!* "Oh, that I were a *glove* upon that hand that I might touch that cheek." Get the connection now? I tossed in that line for pater. Know what he said when he read it? *Romeo and Juliet?* He said, "The nurse was real good but I didn't get the jokes." He also said, "You get much money for this?" and when I told him I got three pounds for the rights he gave me a box on the ear and advised me to wipe off the greasepaint and "get home and help me with the business like your brother." My father, the critic. As for my mother, the Puritan, she wouldn't even read it. Whenever I brought up the subject, she would simply glare at me and say, "Death and damnation!" I could never think of a topper. But isn't that a hell of a thing for a mother to tell her son?

My father at least tried. In fact, there was one play he liked—*Titus Andronicus.* "That part where the girl holds a pot with the stumps of her hands and catches the blood from the men who raped her and then Titus serves them up in a pie for her to eat—that part was *real* good," he would say. But as to my other plays, all he ever said was,

"Well, if that's what the people want . . ." He thought *King Lear* was "silly." Well, *de gustibus non est disputandum*, etc. Meanwhile, don't think you're getting away with anything. Clearly, my father was not an illiterate. He did *read* the plays, didn't he? Do not mock. And butcher me no butchers. My father, dummy, became a landed gentleman and *mayor of Stratford!* That's right—*mayor!* And the Crown granted him a *coat of arms!*

What a beauty, that coat of arms! A gold shield with a band of black across it that bore a spear of gold tipped with silver. And for a crest a silver falcon with outstretched wings brooding on a silver wreath and supporting a spear. Eat your heart out, Marlowe! Hah! You think *my* father was illiterate? *Marlowe's* father signed his will with an "X"! Yes! An "X"!

Heh heh heh. I have a design in mind for a Marlowe coat of arms: twin Tamburlaines crossed in the form of an "X" rampant against a field of plagiarized texts. And how about a motto? How about: "FIGHT FIERCELY CAMBRIDGE!"? Eh? I like it.

Now about my schooling, toads. There now, I've offended you. God love you, you are all God's creatures and not to be blamed for your condition. There, there, leave off wringing of the hands. We cannot all be me. You are wanted. You are needed. Without toads we would be overrun by flies.

School. Stratford had a free grammar school which I attended every weekday, summer and winter, from the time I was seven until I turned fourteen. I'd beetle down Henley Street, execute an Immelmann at the Market Cross, scream "Who is Sylvia?!" at Dawes, the town baker (he was having a "thing" with Mistress Sylvia Leek, bar-

An Immelmann at the Market Cross

maid at the "Raging Gullet" and my screaming gave him fits!), and then walk two long blocks to the Guild Building. That was school—a room upstairs, over the Council Room. One of the best in all of England, my dears. Our masters were top—utterly top. And for good reason. Stratford paid its teachers twenty pounds per a.—*double* the average for even larger towns. Plush, eh? And all Oxford graduates. Class all the way.

At Stratford we had none of your "Look, look, Duncan! See the dagger! See the pretty dagger?" fiascoes. We were expected to have mastered our native tongue *prior* to entering school, and the manner in which we mastered it has been the cynosure of heated, if not abusive, discussion 'twixt myself and the sun-dappled shade of one of your senile lady teachers from the Los Angeles school system in the New World. I mean, I told her what a "hornbook" was—a slab of wood on which a page full of letters had been fastened and covered over with a thin, transparent sheet of horn to protect it from our grubby little paws. Then I explained how we had this crazy idea that if you learned the sounds of the individual letters you could put together the sound of a word and I wish you could have heard her! Incidentally, what is a Communist? She went on about *that* for a while, and then she called me a "dirty old man" and a "hack in Bard's clothing." She also threatened to foster a cult ascribing the authorship of my plays to Sir Francis Drake! Wouldn't "Old Seven-Ten Split" love that, though? Wouldn't he *adore* it? Why, he might even *believe* it! That lace hanky martinet! Were it not for the storm that crippled the Spanish Armada he would have gone down in the records as an even more colossal ass than the one who ordered the Charge of the Light Brigade. A swelling ocean teeming with enemy dreadnoughts and what is our first line of defense doing? *Bowling,* coz, *bowling!*

Of course. Why not? Enjoy, enjoy! I should have written a *play* about it! Ah, what heroic speeches for the actor who played Drake, eh? "This day is called the Feast of St. Gutter-Ball," etc. etc. It stuns the imagination. Well, too late now. Meanwhile, I have introduced the schoolteacher to G. B. Shaw.

There's another one. Shaw. The bearded sneak! He fancies himself a greater playwright than I and doesn't hesitate to say it. In fact, he doesn't hesitate to say much of *anything*. But I handle him, all right. I handle him.

Handling "God"

Whenever I see him I assume an antic disposition, cross my eyes, drop my jaw moronically, and drone, "Tell me again about the alphabet, George." And no matter what he says after that, all I say is "Garn!" Hee! It drives him *mad*, utterly *mad!*

He was absolutely insufferable right after that musical business. I'd say "Garn!" and he'd sing "The Rain in Spain Stays Mainly in the Plain" at the top of his lungs and there was nothing for it then but to jerk his whiskers and run like the wind. But what a cross to bear, eh? Thank heaven for *West Side Story*.

Heh heh heh. I was *waiting* for a reaction. Sacrilege, eh? Well, you are listening to the source, the fountainhead, the horse's mouth. I am entitled. And listen, children: *Hamlet* depicted events occurring in ninth-century Denmark, but you don't think I was demented or arty enough to write the dialogue in ninth-century *Danish*, do you? Wait a minute, wait a minute, *you* just *might*. I'd better make it clear —I wrote it in seventeenth-century English. Can you guess why? I'll give you a hint: my audiences were comprised of *seventeenth-century Englishmen!* Yes. True. I've always been "funny" that way: I tried to write in a language that was immediate and vital to my audiences. Why do you suppose I studied for months with Jimmy before coming over here? Because I adore the sound of mumbling? Eh? You are utterly wet. And goody gum drops for *West Side Story*. "Prithee, woulds't thou" is not for you. *I* wrote that way, yes, but for God's sake that's the way we *talked!* Not the way *you* talk! Not unless you're a *pansy! Are* you?

I favor adaptations. Did a great deal of adapting myself. *King Lear*, for example. I merely updated it from an earlier play. Yes. And now are you ready for it? Can you stand it? Eh? The original version was a *musical comedy with a happy ending!* Heh heh heh. Be my guest. Vomit!

West Side Story. Jimmy saw it. He travels quite freely between your plane and ours. It's taken me years to find the gimmick, but he was able to master it almost the day after he got here. Said he felt some sort of "pull" that "yanked" him back. "Teen-age voices" screaming for him. *I've* never heard them. But I must see to it that Jimmy meets Joan. Meanwhile, Sharks and Jets, eh? Splendid. A good play is a vital organism. It grows. It adapts to new environments, new milieus of the human predicament. Motion pictures? Glorious. Wish I'd had them. Imagine what I could have done with Lear and the storm on the heath! PanaVision? Stereophonic effects? Zoom lenses? Are you completely 'round the bend? It would have been a *gas!*

What? Only the words were important? We preferred to let our imaginations work rather than use scenery? Heh heh heh. Incredible shrinking man, I love you. Really, I love you. You're so dumb you're adorable. In my day we went to the theater for *excitement*, dummy, and we used every special effect in the book! We had killings and maimings on stage that would have kept you awake nights screaming. And as realistic as we could make it. Blood? The stage was *drowned* in it, and none of your damn vegetable coloring, either. When we had blood it was *blood!* We even made a study and discovered that sheep's blood was better for our bleeding effects than ox blood because it ran more freely. Heh heh heh. God, how I love stunning you with this! Listen, remember that scene in Marlowe's *Tamburlaine* where the governor of Babylon is hung in chains and shot by the besiegers? One night when the Admiral's Company was doing it a bullet went wild and killed a pregnant woman in the audience! Pretty powerful imaginations we had in those days, eh? *Eh?*

My hornbook. I loved that hornbook. I don't know

Handling my brother Gil

which I loved more, that or my lucky stone. I think the
stone. Whenever brother Gil got out of line I would bash
him with it. Know something? It *does* look like sheep's
blood. My hornbook was fun, too. Near the Market Cross
in Stratford there used to be a square wooden structure
on pillars supporting the town clock, and encircling it was
a ledge from which I was to dangle my legs comfortably
and watch my father, the patron of the arts, swindling the
conies below me at his glove stall. I'd bring my hornbook
with me. Never could study in solitude. Never could

write in a calm atmosphere, either; always in a tavern, a
kitchen, a hall, a front parlor. At the Market Cross I was
drenched in marvelous, buzzing, swirling sounds, the
hurly-burly cries of the buyers and the sellers. And what
a glorious vantage point for studying character! Character. I was always very strong on that. Or wouldn't you
know? No—no, you wouldn't, you pathetic boobs.
B-O-O-B-S. That's the way I spelled it on my hornbook.
I spelled it often. Also words that I made up and used
later in my plays. Like "honorificabilitudinitatibus."
Love's Labour's Lost, 1594. Know what the word means?

Honorificabilitudinitatibus being
attacked by a shrike

It doesn't mean a damn thing! Some prating ass once called it an anagram for *"Hi ludi F. Baconis nati tuiti orbi"*—which he claims is Arabic for "These plays, the offspring of F. Bacon, are preserved for the world." Keep smirking,

Bacon reading Ovid

swine; it is also an anagram for "F. Bacon reads Ovid in the bathroom." Hah! Know what we did with anagrammers in my day? We burned them at the stake for witches and bloody good riddance!

Anagrammer being burned
at the stake

Heh heh heh. "Little Latin," eh? (I could *kill* Benny for that one!) Well, Halloween, my little sandman. At Stratford School, Latin was *all we studied!* Yes! Cicero, Ovid, Virgil, Livy, Quintilian—the *lot!* The sole purpose of school then was turning out clerks for Church positions, not water skiers for "SurfSide 6." And except for the Bible, the Book of Common Prayer, and some Greek, Latin was *it!* Latin, Latin, Latin, day in, day out until I bled supines and ablative absolutes all over my buckram shoes!

And talk about *dreary!* Except for Ovid, of course. He
was *our* Henry Miller. I drew upon him for my *Venus
and Adonis,* which was rather a flaming success with the
younger crowd. Know what I mean? S-E-X. I made only
one mistake. I should have called it *Tropic of Venus,* and
please! No pious platitudes about "art"! In my day "art"
was not edible. Heh! I can just see myself bursting in on
my producer shouting, "Dick, I've got a great piece of
art for the Saturday matinee!" He would have broken
both my legs and used me as an extra in the next battle
sequence. Honestly, are you out of your *minds?* "Blood!
Lust! Murder! Rape! Gougings! Incest! Sex! War!"
That's what you told a producer. And you always gave
him the billing before you even wrote the play. Like:
"THRILL TO GIANT SPECTACLE AS THE
KING WITH THE 'CHARMED LIFE' BATTLES
THE INCREDIBLE CREEPING FOREST! THRILLS!
THRILLS! THRILLS! MACBETH! MACBETH!
MACBETH!"

Enough of that. Why do you keep digressing? Weren't
we speaking of my education? Eh? "Never mind Latin,"
you reply. "What about the extensive knowledge of geography, history, etc. implicit in your plays? Whoever wrote
them must certainly have been university trained and well
traveled. And you, pathetic William, fit neither of these
categories."

Of course. Right. I agree. Whoever wrote *The Winter's
Tale* knew his geography like the wart on the tip of his
nose. That's why some of the action takes place in a "seacoast" town in Bohemia when there wasn't even a *pond*
within *a hundred miles* of Bohemia! Heh heh heh. Marlowe de Magellan. Balboa Bacon. Sure.

A warlock at history as well, eh? Why not? That's why in *Henry VI* Talbot's death precedes the capture of Joan of Arc, whereas in fact Talbot died *twenty-two years after* Joan's death! Try dramatic license. Go ahead —*try* it, you anagramming apes. Incidentally, do you see yon cloud in shape of a camel?

My plays—*mine*—are *fraught* with errors of both time and place and contain far *less* erudition than the works of almost any of my contemporaries! Who knew history? Who knew law? All I ever studied was *Latin*, for God's sake! If I couldn't decline it, I didn't *know* it!

But you know everything, don't you, Smerdyakov. Do
you also know that the Venice in my *Merchant* doesn't
even vaguely resemble the Venice of my day? And how
about all that crying and schreiing over Shylock's usury?
Do you jest? Usury was not only a *commonplace* in Venice; it was *applauded!*

Yes. *Now* they tell me. I must have missed that some-
how in my "travels" to Venice. I must have been absent
that day, or lying drugged in a gondola with a Venetian
doxy.

Drugged in a Gondola

Dismal gleeks! *God*, how I pity you!

But listen now, boys, maybe we've got something in Shylock. Mayhap we can attribute *him* to our globe-trotting, dumdum, mystery playwright!

Imbeciles! Is that your idea of a Jew? That ridiculous caricature, that scurrilous folk-myth? Heaven heal your kidneys! Shylock is *obviously* the creation of a man who knew *only* the myths; who never *saw* a Jew; who never left England! For Jews were exiled from England during the Middle Ages and when I was writing the law was still

"*Night Riders*" over on my side

in full force. *Bacon* couldn't have limned so unreal a portrait as Shylock. It could only have been done by a stay-
at-home like me—*me!*

Heh. There are some gentlemen in white sheets over on
the other side who are rather fond of Shylock. They are
now and then given to oozing up to me for a fond patting
of my receding hairline. They don't seem to know much
about *Othello*, however, but if you think I'm going to fill
them in, you're crazier than Lear in his underwear. I'm
planning another of my famous introductions, though, the
instant Jomo Kenyatta gets here. I do hope he brings some
more of those nice Mau Mau gentlemen with him. Speaking of bigots, *guess* who's the idol of the night riders over
here! Yes! "Fraternity King" Marlowe! Talk about Shylock! Ever read a play by Marlowe called *The Rose?*
It is the *worst*, the—!

Mark! Stirrings in the neighbor room!

Anon!

TAPE THREE

Aha! The Beard again!

This time he wore a gunbelt over his pajamas and there was a girl with him, a hot-eyed wench in a sheer turquoise nightgown and hiking boots. She held a flashlight at the doorway and as the beam splashed over me she screamed. Perhaps it was because she could see through me, for it is a phenomenon certainly worth thinking about, but actually I think it was because I was—and am—naked as a jaybird. I hope this does not upset you. There is no Hereafter for underwear.

Her screaming rattled me, for I have always fancied myself rather chic sans britches. We all have our little frailties, eh? "And what have kings that privates have not too." etc. etc. *Henry V*, 1599.

The Beard stood mesmerized and *"Por Dios!"* gasped the girl.

And have not Bards privates, too?

That was more like it. More what I'm accustomed to—
awe. I decided to make contact with them.

"Listen, is that Spanish?" I said quickly. "Can you tell
me exactly where I—?"

Blam! Blam! The Beard fired two shots through me, the
girl shrieked, and I faded. If there's anything I can't bear
it's a scene.

Perhaps we will have some peace tonight. But hence-
forth I will have to whisper. *Sotto voce* and all that.

And "now entertain conjecture of a time when creeping murmur and the poring dark fills the wide vessel of the universe." Remember that one? *Hal Five*. Has nothing at all to do with what I was going to say; I merely felt like saying it out loud. Sheer loveliness needs no context, right? And that line, friend, is lovely. Then in 1601 I wrote:

> . . . and then, they say, no spirit can
> walk abroad. The nights are whole-
> some; then no planets strike, nor
> fairy takes nor witch hath power to
> charm; so hallow'd and gracious is
> the time.

Know what I did after I wrote that speech? I hugged myself!

Getting back to "spirits walking abroad" . . . Where were we? Ah, yes. The abundance of erudition in my plays. For instance, how did I know so much about the War of the Roses? How could I even have sorted it out? All I studied was Latin, right? Pungent thinking there, coz. In fact, I'm still not terribly sure about that particular series of plays. Judas priest, I was working from a genealogy chart more complicated than *War and Peace*. Or *Wuthering Heights*. Or *Hawaii*. Incidentally, I once wrote a play in which a war is kicked off by a box of tennis balls, but nine hundred pages about a *pineapple?!*

Heh. Erudition. Look, what if a producer were to hand a Hollywood writer a copy of *Seven Pillars of Wisdom* (By the way, you think *Marlowe* is "queen" of the here-after? Wait 'til I tell you about the "new boy"!) and tell him to come up with a screen play based on that work. By your choplogic—and if you were descended from Mars

Marlowe and T·E·Lawrence,
"The Bedsheet Twins"

and had just seen the picture—wouldn't you be forced to assume that the scenarist had either spent several years in Arabia or been a serious student of Arab history in order to have seemed so effortlessly conversant with his subject? Eh? Well, it wasn't that way at *all!* The writer gleaned his "erudition" from the source, the book. And I took *my* information, *my* settings, *my* facts from *similar* sources. I even lifted my *plots* from other sources: Plautus, Boccaccio, Plutarch, and Gower; Holinshed's *Chronicle His-*

tory of *England, Scotland, and Ireland. Romeo and Juliet*
I lifted from a poem and *Lear, Hamlet, Taming of the
Shrew, As You Like It,* and *The Merchant of Venice* were
adaptations of prior plays with most of the "erudition"
built in. I understand that you call this process "research."
We called it plagiarism. "A rose by any other name," etc.
Romeo and Juliet.

Benny didn't work that way. He also had no seacoasts
in Bohemia. But then Benny was writing for posterity,
whereas I was writing for coin of the realm. Does that
shock you, you pious bugs, you nauseating hypocrites?
Does that shock you? Why, I rarely even had any choice
as to the selection of my material! Heh heh heh. Really
rocks you, doesn't it, that maybe I didn't *want* to write
Hamlet; that maybe I *hated* the idea of *Othello.* What if I
told you, for instance, that I wrote one play because Liz
ordered me to do one "where the fat boy gets the lead
and he falls in love." Well, it's *true,* you fungus, it's *true!
Merry Wives of Windsor.* And when it wasn't Liz bugging
me, it was the theater owners with "Billy, baby, a little
Seneca this time, the town's in an ugly mood," or "Let's do
the mistaken identity bit again Shrove Tuesday, it's always
big before Lent." And everything always in a hurry. That's
why I lifted my plots and characters. Who had time for
originals? Only the BM twins, Bacon and Marlowe. The
college playboys. The amateurs. Oxford, rah! Well, my
group—the Chamberlain's Players—had 84 per cent fewer
originals. You think we were playing games? Eh? We were
making a *living,* dummy, a *living!*

The big money was in acting, not writing. Benny and I
both started out as actors, but the moment he sold his first
play Benny gave it up. Not I. I acted to the very end; I

needed heavy cash for my real estate investments. But you couldn't very well make money acting without *plays,* fatheads, and we burned up material faster than your television. If a new play got six performances in the year it was a *smash.* So I cranked out material like summer lightning in an age when Benny was ribbed for taking as long as five weeks on *one play.* Naturally, my haste produced several unintended comedies of errors. But aren't you glad, you wise armadillos, you modernist scholars? You have made your reputations trying to find sense in my nonsense, purpose in my blunders. What cosmic meanings you've spied in my lapses of memory. My God, now and then I'd even lose track of a character's name and you should see the learned papers that have sprouted from *that!*

Yes, I made mistakes. I am not God. G. B. Shaw is God. Heh heh heh. Like to hear a great moment from my first draft of *Hamlet?* I was getting it ready for the road show—your "Borscht Circuit," I believe—when they gave me a week to finish it. Are you ready for the Great Soliloquy? Eh? Pretend it's a style test. See if you can identify the author:

> To be, or not to be—ay, there's the point:
> To die, to sleep—is that all? ay all. No;
> To sleep, to dream—ay, marry, there it goes;

Sorry, that's where I *always* break up. Tush. I must compose myself. Let us continue.

> For in that dream of death, when we awake,
> And borne before an everlasting judge,
> From whence no passenger ever returned,
> The undiscovered country, at whose sight
> The happy smile, and the accursed damn'd.

Are you *getting* this? Eh? Can you *believe* it? Listen, I'm
not making it up! I was making it up *then*, not *now!*

> But for this, the joyful hope of this,
> Who'd bear the scorns and flattery of the world,
> Scorned by the right rich, the rich cursed of the poor,
> The widow being oppressed, the orphan wrong'd,
> The taste of hunger or a tyrant's reign,
> And thousand more calamities besides . . .

And thousand more calamities *besides!* Look, would you
excuse me for a moment? Whenever I get to that line I
have to go to the bathroom. Not really, of course, but the
reflex is still there.

I wrote in a hurry. Any doubt of that now? But Bacon,
De Vere, and Marlowe *never* wrote in a hurry. They
didn't have to. Bacon and De Vere were nobles and Marlowe had outside income from spy biz. So I will take credit
for both the fame and the blunders. Eh? (If yes, paw the
ground twice. Good show!)

Speaking of blunders, what Burbage and I could have
done with the budget of *Mutiny on the Bounty!* How
many millions was it? Heh heh heh. Know what Dickie
and I would have done with it? We would have closed
down the bloody Globe and scattered like the autumn
leaves to the islands of the South! Dick would have been
free to come of age in Samoa and I would have been free
to write something meaningful. Heh. Shocked you again,
didn't I. I forget you don't know about Dickie and the
ladies. But didn't I trump him once, though? Didn't I?
One night when he was playing the lead in *Richard III* I
overheard him working out a cozy little rendezvous for
later that night with the wife of one of the playgoers. So

Bacon, de Vere, and Marlowe hacking
it out at the furious rate of five
words a day (all of them vomitous)

I whizzed to the rendezvous flat while he was getting off
his makeup, and naturally I charmed the little darling out
of her panties. When Dick finally arrived, he told the man-
servant to announce that "Richard III is here!" But I sent
back word to him that "William the Conqueror comes before Richard III!" Heh heh heh. That was before Dick
turned nasty and broke down the door. Oons, he was a
fun guy!

Phantom Bard Scoring

But soft you now, a final word about my "education."
And I've got a secret! Back in my day we had this wild
new invention called "books." They looked pretty complicated, see, but once you got the hang of it they were
easy to operate. You merely—Am I going too quickly for
you?—You merely (1) opened them and (2) read them.
The reading was the crazy part, but once you got the
hang of that you could (3) extract "information." Lon-

don was the home of the shortcut. Name it and there was a "how-to" book on it, including how to cook, ride, survey land, take spots off velvet, navigate a ship, and what to do "when the physician is not present." *That's* where I got my adult education. Who needed Latin and Greek? Why, we even had books of classical quotations translated into English and arranged under subject matter!

Neat, eh? Heh heh heh. Now you know why I'm so "well informed." Of course, there's still one more contributing factor: I was a genius! And that burns your bloody arse, now, doesn't it!

Still no sounds from the neighbor room. Good. For now we come to the heart of the matter, the *pièce de résistance*. I refer, donkey, to the missing manuscripts.

Where would we be without a little cloak-and-dagger, eh? I mean, how could we survive? To play the game, you merely say: "If Shakespeare wrote the plays, where are the original texts in his handwriting? Texts bearing his signature?" And then your partner, Stupid ⚔2, says: "Isn't it because they were hidden? I mean, isn't that why they've never turned up?" And then the moderator, the Dauphin, says: "Precisely. And they were hidden because they are in either Bacon's or Marlowe's handwriting, and either of these distinguished gentlemen would have been so ashamed of the tripe they had turned out that they paid Shakespeare a lifetime annuity for taking the blame." That's how you play the game.

But I have news for you. I know where the body is buried; where the manuscripts are hidden! They are *not* in Thomas Walsingham's tomb in Kent, which some fantastical dunce ripped apart in 1956, hoping to find texts in Marlowe's handwriting. Na, na—your Uncle Billy knows better than *that*. And soon *you* will know better. For I'm going to *tell!*

Calmly, now. This could lead to a crueler, more vicious squabble over rights than between the Lancasters and the Yorks. Ground rules must be established. And I hereby establish them. I hereby assign all grants, titles, and rights, in and of the original "Shakespearean texts," hereafter referred to as "The Works," worldwide and in perpetuity, to the first man who lays his grubby hands on them!

Now then, you bloody fortune hunter! First you must go to Stratford-on-Avon. Are you there? Excellent. But

Your hunt begins at Stratford

now you must proceed with the utmost caution. The place is infested with assassins and sappers from the Baconian Society and should they scent your intent they will slit you. Mark me! Have a care! Pretend, first of all, that you are a casual tourist. Spend a day or two wandering about the countryside or swilling in the pubs. On the evening of the third day, proceed to the Red Goose tavern. Order the kidney pie and ale. Pure heaven. It will also give you the stomach for what must now be done. For you must proceed to the "Outer Limits" of guile in order to divert suspicion. The means, of course, are optional. But by way of example, if you happen to be an American, an excellent ploy would be to complain loudly and belligerently about the quality of the food, the temperature of the ale, and the inadequacy of the service. Then use that as a springboard into Anglo-American relations, comparative standards of living, etc. Then you must get into World War II, and it is *absolutely imperative* that you refer to Dunkirk as a "bloody balls-up." Try to manage this offhandedly, as you are lifting your glass to your lips. Two phenomena will immediately transpire. The first of these is that several people in shaggy tweed will rise and ooze out of the pub. Do not be alarmed. These will be the Baconians abandoning you as "above suspicion." The second phenomenon, however, may be cause for alarm after all. Several patriots will stun you like an ox. When you have regained consciousness in the River Afton, rejoice. The plan is working! Now you may come and go freely!

Still with me, boys? Good, good, good! Proceed flank speed (someone will read that two hundred years from now and say that "Shakespeare" was a sailor!) to my old house on Henley Street. Since lately it has become a tour-

ist trap, your move will now the more certainly seem in-
nocuous—in fact, purposeless—to "them." We'll fox them
yet, lads, won't we? Won't we? Hah hah! Of course!

Spend the next two days wandering around my house.
Ingratiate yourself with the custodian. Ten pounds should

Buttering up the Custodian

do it. Then use wax and your native ingenuity to take an
impression from the rear door lock. Should the custodian
nab you, tell him you want it as a "souvenir." He will
chuckle inanely. If he does not chuckle you are in serious

trouble. But another tenner should handle it or I am no judge of the British character.

A break from the monotony! To London for the night, where you will have a key made from your wax impression. But back again to the house in Stratford the following morning. Test the key. When you are satisfied that the custodian has not turned vicious and changed the lock on you, return to your quarters and bide your time until nightfall. Under *no circumstances return to the Red*

Now you're in an alley, stupid, Smashed out of your mind

Goose! At six, however, you will slip out to any of the other pubs where I advise you to swill generously, although you should make an effort, in the interest of prudence, to slop most of it onto the floor. Two hours of this should do. Leave. Wander along Henley Street pretending to be drunk. People will be rushing to the Shakespeare Memorial Theater and no one will notice if you bumble silently into the alley and to the back door of my house. If someone does notice they will think you are going to the bathroom. You are safe. Unless, of course, someone greets you at the door as you are entering with your nifty key. A night watchman, perhaps. Should such an exigency arise, I strongly recommend that you fall to your knees blubbering for mercy. However, the likelihood is remote. Upstairs, then, to my bedroom, quickly, quickly! It is marked by a plaque on the door: "Billy S. Slept Here." Don't read all the rest of it, fool, get inside and close the door! Go to the fireplace! The bottom brick, third from the left end on the left side of the hearth —it is loose! Tug, pull, pry it out! Once out, the two on either side of it will slide out like butter! Heh! Getting excited? So am I! Now reach your hand into the hole and you will soon enough feel a package wrapped in oilskin! Pull it out! Gently, coz, gently! And unwrap it with all the love and tenderness of which you are capable! For do you know what you hold in your unworthy but now blessed hands? Eh? What priceless jewel more precious than all your tribe? Of *course!* My *hornbook!!*

Note the arrangement of the letters:

"PHANTOM BARD" STRIKES AGAIN!

Heh heh heh heh heh!

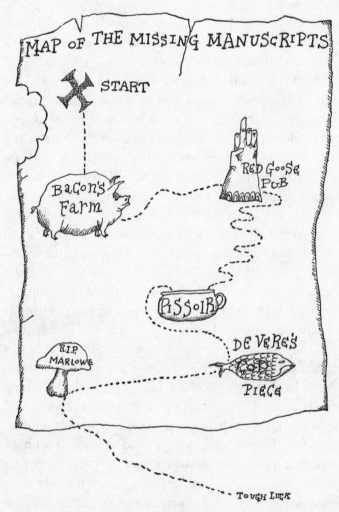

Leprous goons! Lavish warts! Why me? Why pick on *me?* Why not Webster, Jonson, or Dekker?! Have you found *their* original texts? Or *Marlowe's?* In a pig's spleen, you have! In every case where the play found its way into print, there are no extant manuscripts in the handwriting of *any* of my contemporaries! Sweet fumbumbis, who collected autographs? Especially of playwrights? Jesu, we didn't even have authors' luncheons! Who wanted to meet the author? Of the Bible, *yes*, but of *plays?!* Come *on* now, coz! Are you *serious?* Listen, paper was expensive in my day, and once my printer, Mr. Jaggard, had inverted all the u's and n's in my First Folio he promptly used the original texts for gift-wrapping cookbooks. See how a king can go àprogress through the guts of a beggar? *Hamlet*, 1601.

And now to this muck about "how could Shakespeare have written all that courtly dialogue for the nobles in his plays unless he were highly familiar with court life and personnages—in fact, a noble himself?" Marry-gup, you sapient fools, and how can you know that I represented the speech and manners of court *correctly?* What do you know about how the nobles spoke and behaved? Only what *I told you!* And I can assure you that Richard the Three never spoke in iambic pentameter except when drunk, when he would pat his hump and recite obscene limericks. Furthermore, never on his *best day* could Henry V have come up with a line like "the tide of pomp that beats upon the high shore of this world"! The limit of his vocabulary was "Charge!"

Oh, it galls me. But why do I descend to the level of gulldom. Why do I argue with you, eh? You are beneath contempt. Sucks-boo to higher criticism.

I am disturbed by the silence from the neighbor room, coz. Usually I hear heavy breathing but ever since the shooting episode of last night not so much as the sigh of a moth. And yet I sense a presence. Nothing supernatural on my part; I scent the acrid odor of cigar smoke. Who goes there, eh? Art thou officer? Or art thou base, common, and popular?

I don't like it. What will come through that door *this* time? Men in armor? Sir Giles Overreach? Rebecca of Sunnybrook Farm? Eh?

Anon, coz!

TAPE FOUR

I have just undergone an experience the likes of which beggars the imagination. As I faded into the room tonight blinding lights were turned upon me and there commenced such a chattering of machine guns and babbling of voices that it near harrowed up my soul. Over a dozen men in berets and olive drab uniforms were bisecting me with bullets! Couldn't harm me, of course. But I'm still shaking.

I transmigrated back instanter and located Benny, who is extremely analytical about preternatural occurrences. I explained to him what had happened.

"Do you have any enemies?" he asked finally.

"The Baconians," I ventured.

"Oh, don't be an ass, Will!" he snapped. "They don't carry firearms."

"That's all very well for *you* to say," I sulked. "You weren't there."

"'There,'" he mimicked. "You keep saying 'there.' Where the devil is *'there'?*"

"I don't know."

"You don't know," he echoed in a flat monotone.

"No."

His brow was a book in which one might read matters gleep, and he eyed me in silence. Not an eyelash flickered. And when at last he spoke, it was in an oddly muffled voice. "Did it have a seacoast?" he asked.

"I don't know," I muttered quickly. I wasn't being sucked into *that* one again.

"You mean you transmigrated without researching it *first?*" prodded Ben a little irritably, and "Dammit, I came to you for advice, not another bloody lecture!" I erupted. "Ten men with guns blasting away at me and—!"

"*All right!*" he shouted over me. "Now let's start acting like grown men and get to the facts! Where in hell do you *think* you were?!"

"A wood near Spain."

"A—wood—near—Spain."

"Rip Torn," I mumbled.

"*What?!*"

"Nothing." It was the way he'd said it.

Benny eyed me severely. "Now look, Will, let's—"

"Are you going to tell me about the 'unities' again, Ben? Eh? Are you going to—?"

"All I want to know is what makes you think you were in Spain!" he roared.

I told him quietly about The Beard and some snatches of words from the girl. Ben rubbed his chin thoughtfully.

"Describe The Beard again, Will."

I described him. It was one of my more lurid descriptive passages.

Benny's eyes were hoods. "I think you were in Latin America."

"Latin," I whined, "always harping on Latin!"

"Oh, shut up. Now listen, go back to that room right now and if there's anyone still in there just smile real friendly and say, '*Buenos días!*'"

"Are you *mad?* Drake would—!"

"Will-YAM!" he shouted. I knew that look and held my tongue. "Now look," he continued softly, "the key to this situation is communication. You must speak to them in a language they understand."

"Listen, you're telling *me?* You're telling that to *me?* Did I write *Hamlet* in Danish? Eh? Did—?"

"Billy?"

I transmigrated back to the room, said *"Buenos días!"* and was accorded another salvo of gunfire for my pains. I flashed back to Ben.

"What should I say *next* time? 'Jesus loves me'?"

"Eh?"

I told him what had occurred. He puffed up like an owl and looked wise. Then he deflated again. "Look, Will," he said softly, "why not give it up? *We* know you wrote them."

"Does Drake?"

"What?"

"Never mind."

"Don't go back."

"It's the principle of the thing."

"Nonsense," he snorted.

"Buenos días!" I parried.

"Okay," sighed Ben, "go on back. But this time say 'Cuba *sí, Yanqui no.*'"

"Cuba sí, Yanqui no."

"Yes."

"What does it mean?"

"Never mind."

"But—"

"Trust me on this one, will you, Billy?"

"Say it again."

"Cuba sí, Yanqui no."

"Cuba sí, Yanqui no."

"Very good."

I transmigrated. But I was back in a flash.

"I forgot," I told Ben sheepishly. "Say it again, eh?"

"*Cuba - sí - Yanqui - no.*"

"*Cuba sí, Yanqui no.*"

"Bravo!"

"Listen, you won't tell me what it means?"

"About *time* you did your own research."

I faded, reappeared in the room, and quicker than thought roared: "*CUBA SÍ, YANQUI NO!*"

The effect was magical. A staccato burst of machine-

gun fire ceased instanter, and the men in olive green gaped
at me openmouthed. So did The Beard and the girl, who
were now present and in uniform. She looked different in
clothes. I daresay I looked as usual to her.

Troops looking me over

The Beard edged suspiciously toward me and then
gabbled something in what I took to be nervous, excited
Spanish.

I drew myself up coolly—or as coolly as possible con-
sidering my nakedness—and said, "Would you have the

common decency, please, to repeat that in a language I can understand?"

It was a rock. The Beard's eyebrow lifted dangerously and his men, murmuring, hefted their weapons. The Beard hushed them with a wave of his cigar. Then he eyed me wildly.

"Who you are?" he croaked.

Now we were getting somewhere. "It is *I, Billy Shakespeare!*"

"*Who?!*"

I could have killed him. "*Shakespeare!*" I repeated.

"Shokspir!"

"Yes! *William* Shakespeare!"

His eyes narrowed to slits. "From thee C.I.A.?"

"FROM THE *SIXTEENTH CENTURY!*" I bawled.

For long moments thereafter we eyed one another in mutual bafflement. Then The Beard folded his arms.

"Shokspir!" he breathed. It was certainly no worse than Shaxberd.

I stood stock still, fearful lest any sudden movement panic him. I mean, I had this funny feeling that all I had to do was cackle and he would have dropped dead on the spot. But then he surprised me. He padded cautiously to within a yard of me, then suddenly jabbed his cigar through my chest.

"*Madre de Dios!*" he gasped and blessed himself. I was aching to suggest "Angels and ministers of grace defend us!" but the instant I opened my mouth he stepped quickly backward and said, "*Espíritus!*" Then he whipped out his revolver and fired a full clip through me.

"I wish you wouldn't do that," I grumbled. "It's damned silly and a nuisance."

We were not getting along

He hurled his revolver through me, and then whimpered piteously, thrusting out his arms like Iago on the verge of saying, "Who, *me?*"

"What you *wan'* from me?!" The Beard moaned emotionally.

"Look," I said, ignoring the whimpering and the side-to-side swaying of his head. "It's very simple. I just want permission to use your tape recorder. And when I'm through I want you to turn the tapes over to humanity. Publish them and stuff."

He fell to his knees, blubbered, and made strange animal noises. It wasn't getting us anywhere.

"Listen," I said, "I'm on the side of good."

I moved to him with the intention of proving myself harmless and *that*, as Jimmy would say, blew the entire bit. He scuttled from the room like an electrified crab, not even bothering to rise, and the others followed hard upon. The girl threw a backward glance at me from the door and then slammed it shut.

So here we are back together again. Charming, eh?

I don't know what will come of all this. This Beard has a lunatic glittering in his eyes that likes me not. Unpredictable as lice. Know what I mean? My luck, of course. A century of striving to break through and I materialize in Bedlam.

I can hear that grinning bastard Marlowe now: "Nice trip, Billy baby? Eh? See any shows?" Sometimes I think I should have listened to my father. So what was wrong with selling gloves? Hath not a glover eyes? If you prick him, doth he not bleed? *Merchant of Venice*. Maybe I should have listened to my *mother*, God help me!

Speaking of mothers: it is imperative that we leap quickly to a little chatchat about *Hamlet*. I doubt that much more time is left me; not the way things have been going. Even as I speak The Beard is doubtless readying infernal engines. Come, coz, to *Hamlet*. And if I hear so much as one sniveling grunt about Oedipus complexes I can promise you some fairly nasty juju, and that rather quickly. Honestly! Judging from the notions of your so-called "scholars," one gathers that only a psychiatrist can explain why, in such and such a scene, I have written "Enter a Messenger" or even "*Exeunt Omnes.*" What sucking claptrap! What bullfrogging noise! What bastard arse logic!

Let me put it this way: it took me considerably less time to write *Hamlet* than it would take one of your "scholars" to compile a bibliography of works *about Hamlet*. And all because Hamlet delays in his revenge. Is the delay that difficult to understand? Eh? Well, the *groundlings* certainly understood it, because it *played*, dummies, it *played!* Laughs in all the right places, know what I mean? That's how you can tell when they're with it: laughs in the right places. Comic relief. Look, if Hamlet's motivation were as complicated and subtly psychological as you've made it out, why by the time the groundlings had their first foggy clue as to what was going on up there the final *curtain* would have been down. What could have been worse? Ninth-century Danish? Eh?

Leave off your damnable complexes. Hamlet delayed for one reason only: the fact that had he taken his revenge immediately I would have had a one-act play. And who was going to wait two hours in the rain for *that?* Eh? Well, I'll *tell* you who—the bloody demolition crew waiting to chop down the bloody theater for bloody firewood! *That's* who!

So there I was, stuck with this mangy, antiquated plot from an old play. I needed the delay, but the problem was how to make it reasonable and not contrived. And it had to be something up to date, something my audiences could "swing" with, as Jimmy says. The answer was simple. It was a phenomenon then peculiar to our times—the "angry young man."

Heh heh heh. Think you've got the patent on that one, eh? Well, let me tell you something, Jack: we *invented* the angry young man. And Marlowe was the original. The

university wit turned sour by the spectacle of real life outside the ivory tower. Happens all the time. Confront
youthful idealism with the mottled spectacle of life as it
really is, and, Whammo! You've got yourself a cynic. Like
Hamlet. Look, suppose you were nineteen years old and
you'd just found out that your mother is a slut, your uncle
is a murderer, your father is in hell for untold crimes,
your girl has just sent you a "Dear John" letter, and
your mother and your father's killers have just decided
that they were made for each other. Now how would
that grab your pious ideals? In your day, Hamlet would
become either a rapist, a tire stealer, or a Baconian.

Hamlet finding out who he is

So now we have a cynical Hamlet. And now we have a very simple motivation for the delay. Smart College Boy comes home bubbling with ideals and illusions, everyone around him suddenly turns fink, and when the society of which these finks are a part—and in his eyes, *all*—now turns to him and says, "Listen, the code says you're supposed to kill the king; it's customary, *noblesse oblige*, tradition and all that," a part of Hamlet—the cynical part —says, "Are you *kidding*, fellows?" And this is the part of him that delays; the part that feels that in a meaningless

You in the flowered hat

world there can be no meaning in a killing of revenge. And then, too, there would be the problem of explaining it all to Mother.

Naturally, this inner conflict takes its toll of Hamlet. He knows what they taught him on the playing fields of Wittenberg—that one should always severely reprimand the murderer of one's father. But he can't work up the steam, the emotion, to propel him to his revenge. So he invents "tricks" to help him work up a good "hate" against Claudius. Like the "mousetrap" scene. That was a master stroke on my part—filled in a good eight pages. Listen, you think it was easy to get three acts out of a plot that should have ended ten minutes after opening curtain? Eh?

You there, you in the flowered hat. What? Was Hamlet really insane? How the devil do *I* know! I inherited that business from the original and it afforded me a plenitude of gags and lots of filler. It was also good for suspense because you never knew what the hell was going on. Look, don't ask questions, just enjoy!

Oh, why do I even bother? These tapes will probably never get beyond this room. Ech. Another fruitless journey for Margaret.

Aha! Who comes?!

TAPE FIVE

Who—or what—is the United Fruit Company?

This time The Beard entered solus. He was carrying a book. And he was smirking, no longer afraid.

He slithered into a chair behind the desk, winked hugely at me, and blew out a halo of cigar smoke. He tapped the book. "I know who you," he syruped slyly in that deplorable accent. He flipped the book open to a portrait print of myself, the one with the receding hairline.

"You *Shakspir!*" exulted The Beard.

Had he said "Bacon" I would have incinerated him on the spot.

"Shakspir de writer!" he added.

"And *actor!*"

"*Sí*. I haav make a beeg research on you."

Research! Has the universe gone *mad* over this fetish for facts?!

He jabbed his cigar through me gingerly, as though to

reassure himself that I was indeed a phantom. (I *adore* that word!)

"Don't do that!" I snapped.

"Ta-ta-ta!" he chided. "Do not make for yourself an excitement."

"Well, do not make for yourself an ashtray of me!"

He slammed shut the book. And looked sly. "What you *wan'* from me?"

"I told you," I said austerely. "I am dictating a vital message to the world on your tape recorder. And I would like to continue undisturbed until I am quite finished. Then I want you to promulgate the material in the tapes. Incidentally, I shall also require the services of a notary public."

"Ah!" he said, vacant-eyed.

"Could you be a little more definite?"

"Eh?"

"Well, yes or no? Will you cooperate or shall I 'hant' you? Chains, eerie footsteps, the whole thing." I was bluffing, of course, but as Jimmy says, "no guts no glory."

"What you make weeth thee tape?" he sidestepped. It was difficult to tell whether I had succeeded in frightening him or not.

"I'm attempting to prove once and for all that I wrote my plays."

He suddenly chilled. "You *not* write them?!" he pounced and "I DID write them!" I roared.

This seemed to calm him. "That eez good," he chuckled obscenely. Odd how he reminds me of Marlowe. Is it the messianic glint in his eyes, or the glimmering of Machiavelli?

"Now what about it?" I demanded.

He smiled evilly, puffing on the cigar. Then he pulled it out of his mouth and carelessly flicked an ash to the floor. "Hokay. But firs' you haav to do favor for *me*."

The Beard offering a deal

Marlowe to the teeth!
"What?" I asked warily.
"I wan' you to write for me a play."
"A *what?*"
"A play. What you theenk, eh?"
Well, I thought he was mad, utterly mad, but if you

think I was going to tell him that you're laboring under a magnificent obsession. I thought of the tapes and said, "What *kind* of play? Tragedy? Comedy? History? Pastoral? Pastoral-comical? Historical-pastoral? Tragical-historical? Tragical-comical-*historical*-pastoral? Eh? What kind?"

That was my first mistake. For now he stood up, raving, and launched into a tortured, screaming, two-hour harangue over political history that left my brain reeling.

The Beard throwing a tantrum

Talk about tearing a passion to tatters! He climbed the desk, ripped the drapes, pounded the wall, pounded his *head* against the wall, and moaned like some strange animal in pain. My God, how Kyd would have adored him for Hieronimo in *The Spanish Tragedy!*

"Look," I said at last, trying to break it up, "do not saw the air too much," whereupon he bellowed something about a "United Fruit Company," spreadeagled his arms, and screeched, "Dey are *trying to croocify me like dey croocified Christ!*" Then he fell to the floor, weeping and moaning piteously. It was a little embarrassing.

"Listen," I said, "there's certainly a great deal in what you've said and I'd like to think about it."

Suddenly my hair stood on end. He had pulled himself up to a sitting position and with the tears streaming down his face he had begun to *sing!*

I faded instanter.

Ben couldn't make much sense of my story. "A play?" he marveled.

"A *screen* play."

"Hmmm. Tempting."

"Are you serious? Listen, you think *Fellini* is wild? You should—

"What's the plot?"

"I don't know. All I could make out was the title."

"Namely?"

"*Victory at the Bay of Pigs.*"

Ben whistled softly. "And I thought *Beggar's Bush* was a stinker!"

"That's neither *hic* nor *ibi*."

"Hey, that's *Latin!*"

"Oh, shut up. The question is, what should I do?"

"Research it," said Ben.

"Is that your answer to *everything*, for God's sake?!"

"All right, all right! Go ahead! Write it! One *more* disaster certainly isn't going to tarnish your—!"

I faded on him before he could finish it.

Back in the room, The Beard was waiting. He was still on the floor.

"Listen, about this play," I began; "I'm not much on originals." And then his fit came upon him again. This time, however, I was able to piece out what he wanted. Basically, a patriotic play of the type of *Henry V*. I was to begin with the struggles of a young, idealistic, bearded revolutionary holed up in the mountains of his country and fighting to free his people from the tyrannous "United Fruit Company," the latter to be headed up by someone resembling Richard III. (He insisted on the hump, too.) Then the young idealist comes to power and brings beneficent rule and reform to his formerly oppressed people; specifically, he closes the "night clubs." And then he is viciously attacked by a malevolent power from the north at the Bay of Pigs. Outnumbered seven to one, the idealist's brave little band of defenders repulses the aggressors, like Hal at Agincourt. Over and over, The Beard kept coming back to one point and I can't for the life of me fathom its significance. He said the enemy attack at the bay must be depicted as accompanied by overwhelming air support. "Fill dee screen weeth airoplanes!" he screeched at one point. He referred to it as "air cover." When I probed as to the name of the "enemy power" he told me we would "fill in the names later."

"Look," I said when he was finished, "I'm not too sure I'm the one to write this."

Beard blowing Bard out of the water

He got up off the floor, picked up the tape recorder,
and walked with it toward the door.

"For Jesus' sake, for*bear!*" I yipped.

He turned and glowered at me. "Thee play ees thee
thing," he snarled. Then, "*Homblet,*" he added; "1601."

I threw up right then and there. Ectoplasm, of course,
but highly effective. Meanwhile, no more tapes for a
while. Anon, coz. As usual, my producer wants the script
yesterday.

TAPE SIX

Where have I failed me? Eh?

Two nights ago I began work on *Flaming Victory at the Bay of Pigs*. (Yes. There has been a title change.) I quickly completed the blocking, for all that was required was a variation of my Standard Plot #4: "Attacks by overwhelming forces." Then I plunged into the heroic speeches by the hero, for The Beard was most insistent that these be tackled first (he mumbled something about "adapting" them for television speeches). I was experiencing considerable difficulty with the one that begins, "Once more unto the breach, dear *amigos*, once more, or close the wall up with our bearded dead . . ." etc. etc. when Beard One crept into the room on his little rhino feet and leered over my shoulder at the manuscript.

"What part *now?*"

"It's the 'night before the invasion' scene," I explained wearily. "The one where you wander among your troops disguised as a guava jelly vendor, boosting their morale. 'A little touch of Castro in the night,' etc. etc. Listen, while you're here let's have the name of the 'heavy' again."

a little touch of Castro in the night

"Prazeeden Uniyed States," he spat.
I blinked. "United States?"
"*Sí.*"
"Look here, are you telling me that it was the United *States* your little island beat off?"

"*Sí!*"

"Didn't they win World War II?"

"*Sí!*"

"*Sí!*" I mimicked. "What do you mean, '*Sí!*'?! What the hell am I supposed to be writing here, *A Midsummer Night's Dream?!*"

"I haav geev you thee *focts!*" he screeched. "What you wan' from me, hah? You wan' me to *keel mysalf?*"

"That will not be necessary," I said curtly.

His gay reply took the form of his ripping out a handful

of his beard and thrusting the evil mass under my nose. "*These* are focts, *no?!*"

Somewhere I had lost the thread and was consequently hard pressed for reply. But none proved necessary, for now he fell back against a wall, spreadeagled his arms, and with his head lolling from side to side he commenced his usual moaning, whining, and mystical babbling. Positively astounding. Falling sickness in the vertical. He slumped to the floor, moaning, and presently two men in olive drab came in and carried him out, performing their task with the grace of long usage. Then The Beard's doxy entered, locked the door behind her, and confronted me at the desk. "Are you going ahead with this?" she whispered. Odd! No trace of an accent!

"You speak English very well," I commented.

"Don't do it!" she pleaded.

"Don't do *what?*" I rattled, and "Shhhhh!" she replied, putting a finger to her lips.

Suddenly I became wary. "Are you by any chance a Baconian?"

"What is a Baconian?"

"A maddened swine charging."

"I don't understand you."

"Good. Now what is it you want? A sonnet? Book report? Term paper? What?"

She eyed me levelly, an unnecessary precaution since the desk concealed my nakedness full to the waist. "Do you know what propaganda is?" she asked.

"You poor thing, I *invented* it," I told her. "What do you think my *Henrys* were?"

"Did you know the Doctor plans to use your screen play for sinister propaganda purposes?"

"Who the devil *are* you?"

"C.I.A.!" she snapped. And then she went into *such* a *story!*

"Mr. Shakespeare," she ended it, "you must go back where you came from! Forget about this play!"

"And forget about my tapes?! If I don't write the play, what happens to my tapes?!"

"Leave immediately and I will smuggle the tapes to the United States! Their contents will be published in full!"

"Really?"

Doxy grappling with Bard

"Yes!"

"No cuts, no sneaky editing?"

"My word is my bond!"

"Your *word!* I don't even know your *name!*"

"I am Consuelo Gauze."

"You poor thing," I murmured. "You poor, poor thing."

And then it overcame me. Lethargy, melancholia. I am weary, coz, weary. And so I have commended my tapes and some rough sketches of my contemporaries to the eager Miss Gauze. I don't care any more. Benny was right. The plays are the thing, not who wrote them. I suppose.

This is it, coz. Parting is such sweet sorrow, etc. Will you miss me, you scabrous rogues? Eh? Will you miss me?

Adieu! Adieu! Remember meeeeeeeeeeeee!

Heh heh heh. *Hamlet*, 1601.

FIN